JOAN TOWER

TRES LENT

(Hommage à Messiaen)

for Cello and Piano

AMP-8080

First Printing: January 1995

Associated Music Publishers, Inc.

DISTRIBUTED BY

HAL•LEONARD™
CORPORATION

7777 W. BLUEMOUND RD. P.O. BOX 13819 MILWAUKEE, WI 53213

Très Lent was written as an *hommage* to Olivier Messiaen, particularly to his *Quartet for the End of Time,* which had a special influence on my work.

When I was the pianist for the Da Capo Chamber Players, we frequently performed Messiaen's quartet over a seven-year period. During this time, I grew to love the many risks Messiaen took—particularly the use of very slow "time," both in tempo and in the flow of ideas and events. *Très Lent* is my attempt to make "slow" music work. It is affectionately dedicated to my long-time friend and colleague, who never stops growing as a musician and cellist, Andre Emelianoff.

—JOAN TOWER

*Très Lent was premiered on May 8, 1994
by Andre Emelianoff, cello, and Joan Tower, piano,
at Merkin Concert Hall in New York City.*

Duration: ca. 9 minutes

*Recording: New World Records, CD–80470–2,
Andre Emelianoff, cello, Joan Tower, piano*

to Andre Emelianoff
TRES LENT
(Hommage à Messiaen)

Joan Tower
1994

JOAN TOWER

TRES LENT

(Hommage à Messiaen)

for Cello and Piano

Cello

AMP-8080

First Printing: January 1995

Associated Music Publishers, Inc.

DISTRIBUTED BY

 HAL•LEONARD
CORPORATION

7777 W. BLUEMOUND RD. P.O. BOX 13819 MILWAUKEE, WI 53213

Cello

to Andre Emelianoff

TRES LENT
(Hommage à Messiaen)

Joan Tower
1994

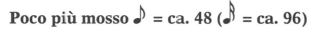

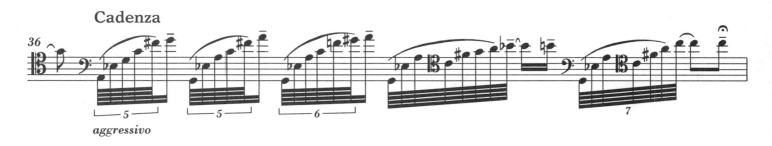

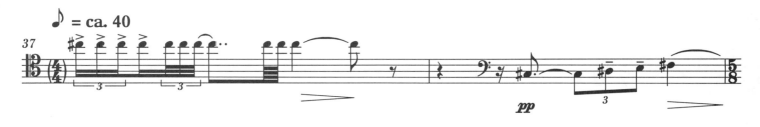